HAVE YO
OUR C

By

REG FRARY

With illustrations by
MADELEINE R. PARKER

NORHEIMSUND BOOKS AND CARDS
1 Whitney Road,
Burton Latimer,
Kettering
Northamptonshire
NN15 5SL

© Reg Frary 1992

First published in 1992

By the same author

DON'T UPSET THE CHOIR
DON'T BLAME THE ORGANIST
NEVER MIND THE VICAR
LAUGHTER IN CHURCH
ANCIENT AND MODERN
WHAT ABOUT THE CHOIR, VICAR?

ISBN 0 948852 33 X

Printed by Peter Dawes Printers
6 Canon Street, Kettering, Northamptonshire
Tel: (0536) 85524   Fax: (0536) 412032

TO ALL ORGANISTS WHO HAVE TO PUT
UP WITH THE VICAR, AND ALL VICARS
WHO HAVE TO PUT UP WITH THE
ORGANIST – AND ALL CHOIRS WHO
HAVE TO PUT UP WITH BOTH OF THEM.

HAVE YOU HEARD OUR CHOIR?

ASSAULT AND FLATTERY

FOR MOST of the time the only thing on the notice board at my cousin Henry's village church in unknown Lincolnshire is a drawing pin. They don't expect visitors from the outside world at Henry's church. And as Henry once told a forbidding lady walker who had lost her way and who collared Henry outside the church to demand to know where on earth she was and how long had such a fine church been abandoned, to announce the church service times to the locals on the notice board would be rather like sticking a notice on the pub door reminding customers of the opening times. Everybody in the place knew them – had known them from childhood.

There is, however, one exception to the normal barrenness of the notice board at Henry's church. Each year, a week or two before Christmas, the choir put on their seasonal show for charity. This consists of some very informal singing, vaguely connected with Handel's "Messiah". The event is always advertised by a large poster, completely covering the notice board, which is the work of the organist's granddaughter who loves horses but not the children who ride them and is a very successful illustrator of children's books. It is bordered by fat cherubs, bulbous Father Christmases and horses' heads and proclaims: "Highlights from Messiah – come and join in. Bring your own music. Thanksgiving collection for charity".

How and why the event originated is lost history. The choir say they've always done it. The parish is full of such

5

traditions and all are unassailable as a recent new vicar was forced to realize to his sorrow. He had suggested to the church council that, in the cause of inter-parish fellowship and co-operation, after the next "Messiah highlights" the event should be replaced by a concert by the Ladies' Madrigal Society from a neighbouring village.

At that year's "Highlights" performance more than twice the usual number of parishioners – with their music – turned up to take part, and one or two who couldn't lay their hands on a "Messiah" were seen with "Elijah" or "The damnation of Faust" under their arms. The message was clear. The new vicar capitulated in the face of tradition even to the extent of enthusing over the revered annual custom of the three-hour peal of bells (the bell tower is a few feet from the vicar's bedroom window) from nine pm until midnight in celebration of the organist's birthday.

Despite this joyous prolonged tribute, however, no one really seems to know how old the organist is. No one in the choir can remember when he wasn't there and he presents a very well-preserved appearance. In fact he is so well-preserved that he doesn't seem to have grown any older for years. Like his organist's gown, his Sunday buttonhole, his car and his choice of music, he never changes and all this makes his choir – one of the last all-male strongholds in the Church of England, it would seem – a very comfortable and pleasant organization to belong to, particularly if you can't read a note of music and don't understand musical terms and find it difficult to spot the place in the anthem where you are supposed to come in. He explains things in everyday language that even the most unmusical choir member can understand. When, for instance, the tenors get to sound too much like an enraged football crowd in a passage of music marked *tranquillo*, he remarks mildly

"Now we don't want it a yard wide, do we? Put the brakes on a bit", and if the treble soloist is missing the point entirely, he recommends gently "It'll help, lad, if you turn to the right page – and then put some beef into it".

And now, once again, Christmas was approaching and yet another "Messiah highlights" was in the offing. I had come to stay with cousin Henry for the occasion and we had had our final rehearsal and were looking forward gleefully to the performance in two days' time (the most gleeful anticipation of the choir, as usual, being the result achieved when the congregation joined them in rendering the Hallelujah chorus).

And then the blow fell.

Some kind of virus had hit the village with lightning speed and, although most of the men of the choir appeared to have evaded it, every one of the boys was reported out of action.

On that Saturday evening the organist called an emergency meeting of the men in the vestry and it soon became very clear that the performance would have to be cancelled – an unthinkable calamity. Even Ancient Abel couldn't help in this situation although Abel is unique. It is not possible to pinpoint what kind of voice he has. Strictly speaking his is not a conventional voicebox; it's more of a super-adaptable piece of apparatus capable of producing almost any kind of sound imaginable. And this makes him very useful when the choir is short of an alto, tenor or bass. I've heard him produce the most ear-splitting falsetto with the utmost ease and his huge Chaliapin-like bass voice is just as devastating, while his sobbing Italian tenor is one of the most moving sounds I know. In fact my cousin Henry says it moves people away as far as possible in no time at all. But even Abel couldn't imitate a dozen trebles.

It was at this last bewildering moment that the vicar bounced into the vestry, full of enthusiasm and kind thoughts. Everything was going to be all right. We needn't worry. He had been on the phone to the Ladies' Madrigal Society – the one, we would remember, that he had suggested should give a Christmas concert as an alternative to the "Messiah highlights". All the ladies were very willing to help the choir out of its difficulties. It would be such a splendid exercise in inter–parish fellowship and co-operation ...

Long after the vicar had gone, the choir men sat in a stunned silent circle. Presently it started to get dark and we could hardly see the dismay on each other's faces. Abel got up slowly, still in a state of shock, and automatically switched on the vestry light which promptly fused. Trance-like, he moved to a surviving gas lamp over the piano. Without a glance at it, he lighted it with his pipe lighter. It whistled and flickered. He came back to the rest of the group, who were all gazing unseeingly at the floor. "It's come to this", grated Abel. "It's actually come to this. Women in our choir!"

"Never been known", fumed out bass soloist.

"Women!" echoed Henry, hollowly.

"Handel had women in the choir at the first performance of 'Messiah' in Dublin", I offered, meaning to be helpful. I immediately realized my awful bloomer.

"This is not Dublin and Handel's got nothing to do with our 'Messiah' performance", reprimanded the organist. "Things have got a bit different since his day – they have here, anyway. If Handel heard our choir, he wouldn't want women butting in. He'd realize ..."

We didn't hear what Handel would realize about our choir, for at that point the vicar, still all helpful smiles, put his head round the door. "I've just arranged for a coach to pick up the ladies tomorrow evening", he announced. "Isn't it splendid?" He was too elated to notice the state of the assembled company. He turned to leave and noted the lighted gas lamp. He gave an amazed chuckle. "Good heavens, I didn't know that thing still worked. It takes me back to the church where I was a choir boy. We still had gas lighting there. It's funny how the church hangs on to old-fashioned ideas long after everyone else has gone ahead". He still didn't notice the state of the assembled company ...

When I arrived at the church on the evening of the performance, the Ladies' Madrigal Society, all dressed in their black "concert" dresses and carrying their "Messiah" copies and large bulging handbags, were grouped at one end of the vestry and our choir men were lurking at the other end. In the wide space between them the vicar ambled up and down, rather aimlessly I thought, smiling vaguely as he threw out cheerful remarks to both sides, trying to bring them together. He wasn't being very successful, although one very attractive girl from the ladies' camp did brave our countenances and venture across the divide to say how very much she admired our red cassocks, which looked so much better than those used by the choir of her church, which were black, mostly turning green. She addressed herself particularly to one of our younger and more impressionable tenors, who in return started enthusing about her dress until he suddenly became aware of the looks of his colleagues and promptly backed in confusion into the cassock cupboard.

And so, for the first time ever, ladies sang in the choir in my cousin Henry's church. As usual the place was packed and, despite the untraditional make-up of the choir, the congregation at least – in the words of the rather superior vicar's warden – "thoroughly enjoyed themselves murdering Handel".

"and if we kept on pushing against the table, the whole thing would collapse and we'd get nothing"

In the vestry afterwards the vicar congratulated the choir on leading another unusual, indeed refreshingly different, performance of "Messiah" and added a very special word of thanks to the Ladies' Madrigal Society who, after all, had saved the day and ensured that a well-loved local tradition was not broken. He then invited us all to partake of a little light refreshment before we bade farewell to our guests, so we all crowded round a small trestle table behind which were two very large cross-looking ladies who said that we had finished much earlier that we did last year and the water for the tea and coffee had not yet boiled, so we'd have to wait – and if we kept on pushing against the table, the whole thing would collapse and we'd get nothing. So we all backed off and talked together and nibbled mince pies, which tasted strongly of dripping, until the tea and coffee materialized and we were all able to wash away the dripping taste and see the ladies off in their coach.

When they had gone, the choir men returned to the church to "clear up the choirstalls", which seemed to consist of sitting around in the vestry and watching Abel trying to light his pipe – something I had never seen him accomplish. At the end of a long quiet period, during which Abel made three or four dozen attempts to achieve his aim and his lighter finally gave up, obliging him to use a candle taper which proved equally ineffective, the young tenor in the admired red cassock said "She's right, you know – these *are* smart cassocks – very smart".

To my surprise he met with no rebuff. The organist said slowly "Apparently the organ in the church where this madrigal lot come from is very fine – very big. The only trouble is they haven't got a proper choir – no men. They reckon that if we did our 'Messiah highlights' there next year, as well as here, it would be a roaring success. The church is bigger than ours and they said we'd fill it to the doors".

"One of them told me that it was absolutely thrilling singing with such a professional male voice choir as ours", said our alto, who was still nibbling cautiously at one of the dripping mince pies. "It was the blonde one with the big red bow."

"Big red bow where?" asked Henry.

"On her head", said the alto.

11

"Ah, it was the other one who spoke to me, then", clarified Henry, "the one with the bow round her neck. She said her brother was something to do with the recording business and she could get him interested, if we sang in their church next year".

"What about our boys? They must come too", put in the bass soloist.

"Of course", confirmed the organist, "us, the boys and the madrigal crowd – and their great big organ. The lot! Lovely!"

"Nice crowd, really", mused Henry. "Sing well – appreciate us".

Abel at last gave up his attempts to light his pipe. He tapped it out all over the heating stove. "Women!" he growled.

WAYS AND MEANS

GROANER, THE organist and choirmaster at the church where my cousin Jack is in the choir, never says a kind word to his choir. After every service in which the choir takes part he joins them in the vestry and shouts things like "Well, I've heard a few pathetic efforts in my day, but this beats everything" or "I was ashamed – *ashamed* – to be sitting there in charge of you lot" or "Call yourselves a choir! – load of rubbish". Then as he walks home and is invariably waylaid by enthusiastic members of the congregation, who congratulate him on the music at the service, he accepts their praises with genteel modesty and generously attributes any success to "my very loyal and accomplished singers, who I appreciate so much".

During choir practice he never fails to tell the choir how very superior his singers of twenty and thirty years ago were, quite forgetting that these *are* his singers of twenty and thirty years ago. He's been in charge for years and years, and everyone stays with him for years and years.

Groaner's church forms one side of a delightful square in a small West country market town in a lively parish which boasts rather larger congregations than are usual these days. Sunday services include what is known as The Great Popular Family Service, to which everyone is always warmly welcomed, and choral Matins, to which no one is ever welcomed, warmly or otherwise. However, there are a number of diehards, formal people, who prefer not to dance in the aisles and hug each other or clap hands and stamp and knock balloons about the church while singing hymns, and these continue to come to

13

Matins, much to the sorrow of the forward-looking young vicar, who lives in hopes that as the diehards die off he will be able to discontinue Matins and channel all comers into the joy of The Great Popular Family Service.

Unfortunately there are those who enjoy the Prayer Book language and the kind of music used at Matins and, if anything, their numbers are growing despite the vicar's larger and larger multicoloured posters advertising The Great Popular Family Service, which now completely cover the weatherbeaten notice board with its minute Matins announcement.

Groaner's choir don't sing at the Family Service and the organ is ignored. The vicar prefers everyone to be as informal and partylike as possible and to bring guitars and drums, and sometimes there's lots of happy stereo music or someone plays the xylophone. But the choir don't waste their time while all this is going on; Groaner conducts choir practice in the vestry and tells the choir what he thinks of them until the church is tidied up after the jollifications of The Great Popular Family Service and is ready for Matins.

Whenever I visit my cousin Jack, it is taken for granted that I'll be singing in the choir at Matins, and on this sunny July morning I was as always looking forward to the opportunity. We had just finished the practice and Groaner had lived up splendidly to his reputation of affectionately insulting everyone for a solid hour. Finally he grated "That's that, then. Goodness knows why those Matins people stick it week after week, putting up with you lot. Mad, or martyrs, I reckon. Anyway, I suppose the circus has moved out of the church now, so we'd better get things organized".

As Groaner clambered behind the choir stalls and opened

14

up the console with a great rattling of keys and thumping of jammed doors, and two of the choir boys started distributing the music in the choir stalls, the last of The Great Popular Family Service revellers were meandering out of the church towards the coffee room, trailing small laughing or bawling children with deflating balloons and the remains of coloured streamers. One little girl sprawled in the doorway, red pencilling a huge villainous-looking moustache on a poster picture of a pop star; and a wiry-looking little lady, struggling along behind an armful of home-made banners, who was shouting at everybody about not missing a very special parish get-together on Tuesday evening, fell over the little girl and shouted even louder.

Five minutes later the doorway had been cleared and the appearance of the verger, a regal black-clad figure with immaculate imperial beard, and a well set up churchwarden in stylish pin-striped suit, standing by a pile of prayer books and Hymns Ancient and Modern, set the correct scene for Matins.

The church's fine peal of bells started to ring and the Matins congregation began arriving, discreetly acknowledging each other, and then settling down to see what the vicar had done to the latest parish magazine. It was not, of course, actually called the parish magazine nowadays. Since the arrival of the vicar two years ago, he had changed its name with almost every issue. The latest one, in fact, had no name. Instead, there appeared on the cover a photograph of the vicar pointing at you in the style of the famous First World War recruiting poster and saying WE WANT YOU.

The choir were robed and waiting when the vicar bounced in grasping half a mug of coffee and smiling vigorously. "Splendid gathering at the Family Service this

"Devoted to Alfie, he is"

morning", he enthused. "Really terrific discussions going
on in the coffee room. We're all so ..."

"We're late", grated Groaner. And forthwith we
processed into the chancel and Matins proceeded on its
decorous way without a hint of balloons, banners,
streamers, clappers or stampers. The first hymn, "Through
all the changing scenes of life", went well, although the
vicar seemed to be gazing in puzzlement at the words in

his book, which he made no attempt to sing. He seemed equally puzzled by the Venite and the psalm but, surprisingly, he cheered up tremendously when he came to read the first lesson, which was all about Samson getting his own back on some very unsavoury characters by pulling down a whole temple on them. My cousin, who sat next to me, explained that the vicar was really into dramatics like that. There was a lot of the actor in him; indeed it had been a toss-up whether he'd go into the church or on to the stage.

When we came to the sermon, the vicar stuck to the rules and clambered into the pulpit, although he didn't like the idea of sermons. At The Great Popular Family Service he walked up and down the main aisle and conducted what he called "an in-depth discussion amongst the family". At Matins he preached to the congregation.

As he got into his stride, telling the congregation that the church must look ahead and not be bound by tradition but must experiment with new forms of worship vital to today's needs, Jack leaned close to me and, in a whisper that could be heard at the other end of the church, said "He's not a bad sort really. He's got these funny ideas, that's all, but everyone likes him and he seems to like everyone – animals and all. Devoted to Alfie, he is".

I knew who Alfie was. I could see him sitting fatly under the pulpit steps – a huge black and white cat with a knowing expression and a red velvet collar. "Alfie likes Matins better than the Family Service", Jack's huge whisper informed everyone. "He used to come to the Family Service, but a few weeks ago they had some huge balloons to celebrate the vicar's birthday – not the ordinary ones – real monsters – and Alfie tackled one and it went off with such an explosion that it nearly frightened the life out of him. So now he comes to this service. You don't get that kind of thing at Matins – not cats being blown up by balloons".

The service ended with "Guide me, O thou great redeemer" which, as Jack remarked, didn't seem to grab the vicar any more than the other Matins hymns, and then Groaner played us out with the mighty strains of a Wagner grand march. The vicar hurried to the back of the church to see the congregation off. Unlike his style at The Great Popular Family Service, he didn't hug the women and slap the men on the back and call them "Gert" and "Joe". At Matins you always shook hands and addressed people with the correct style and, as far as the vicar could see, you always would.

The vicar came back into the vestry as the last of the choir were leaving. Dutifully he beamed and thanked them for all their hard work and then, releasing himself from his clerical collar, made his way to the coffee room in hopes that some of the Family Service members would still be there, continuing the in-depth discussion. They weren't. They were all sitting round little tables outside the coffee shop on the other side of the square and all talking at once. He hurried to join them, an unrestrained beam of pure joy breaking through the formal Matins smile.

IN PASSING

I MOVED noiselessly along a soft earth path towards the cosy slumbering village church which I'd suddenly come upon during a walking holiday in Oxfordshire. It was early afternoon on a warm, quiet August day. In the stillness the tiny sounds of insects in the tall, dry churchyard grass enhanced a deep remote peace. I peeped into the cool dimness of the church. Silence. I stepped inside and closed the huge door soundlessly and found myself tiptoeing up the aisle. If I'd had a companion with me, I'd have been whispering "Isn't this delightful?"

At that moment of ancient calm I was certainly not expecting the Grand March from "Aida". But that is what it was. It burst forth from the organ with all the power of its pomp and splendour and continued flamboyantly to its climax. Its final chords rolled regally round the church and dissolved into an utter silence, as if they had never been.

Moments later a shuffling came from the organ and the sound of a jaunty male voice singing "Woman is fickle". The singer – an elderly, rotund, cheerful-faced man – materialized in the choirstalls and immediately spotted me.

"I enjoyed the voluntary", I enthused.

"For a wedding at four o'clock", beamed the organist. "Very nice for getting out of the church with after the ceremony. You need something a bit longer than the old Mendelssohn wedding march these days. The couple can't just walk out straight down the aisle like they used to. Nowadays people jump out at them from pews and from behind pillars and from under the font with cameras and loads of video equipment and until the happy pair have grinned and giggled to everyone's satisfaction they can't get out of church. I've often had to play the Grand March twice before we've finally got rid of them and sometimes even then I've had to slip in 'Moonlight and roses'".

Observing my interest in the organ, the organist warmed to the subject and invited me to look at the console. It was obvious that the instrument was well looked after and that the oak case was very fine indeed. "It's called The Stopper Organ", he explained. "It was given late last century by a man who made a lot of money making stoppers for beer bottles. There's a memorial plaque to him behind the radiator in the vestry".

Sitting in the choirstalls we enjoyed a most interesting half-hour chat about organists and choirs and their traditional difficulties with the contrariness of backward-looking old vicars and forward-looking young ones, until the organist suddenly noticed the time and hastily rose. "The wedding!" he reminded himself. "People will be poking around in here soon. I'm sorry to rush away ..." A sudden thought struck him. "I wonder ..." he speculated. "You're a choir man, you say. I don't suppose you'd help us out by coming in the choir for this wedding? We're going to be awfully short. We're right in the middle of the holiday season and a lot of our choir people are away. What do you say?"

I said I'd be absolutely delighted to help out. "There's nothing I'd like better", I assured him. "By the way, I'm an alto".

"Never mind", he encouraged. "Most of the stuff we're doing will be in unison".

He took me into the vestry, which was a curtained-off space behind the organ filled with what looked like the unsuccessful remains of half-a-dozen jumble sales packed into half-a-dozen large cardboard boxes. They overflowed with old cardigans, odd shoes, coat hangers and a variety of battered kettles and saucepans. The organist said there'd just be time to make us a cup of tea, and from under a historic sink full of flower vases and milk bottles he dislodged a kettle infinitely more battered than the jumble sale leftovers, which he filled from a huge dripping brass tap and placed on a gas ring on what I imagined was the vicar's desk. From a row of mugs ranged along the top of the vestry piano – a forbidding black monster with elephantine legs – he selected two as big as jam jars, which were both presents from somewhere or other, and in no time at all we were sitting on a large dusty table (there being no discernible chairs in the place) enjoying what was to me at least a very welcome cup of tea.

We were soon disturbed. Choir members now started arriving and rummaging behind us on the table amongst what I thought was just another pile of jumble sale leavings. This pile, however, proved to be the choir's robes and it was quite fascinating to see how quickly each member disentangled his or her robes and deftly donned them. A total of half-a-dozen singers eventually turned up – four men and two ladies – and the organist having introduced me to them as a kind of wandering minstrel and fitted me out in a voluminous candle-grease-encrusted cassock and a choirboy's surplice, we were ready for the wedding.

Although the time was four o'clock there seemed to be no sense of urgency. In the manner of brides this one had not yet arrived, and in any case the vicar, who was doubtless very used to the ways of brides, hadn't arrived either. He was a keen gardener, the organist explained, and his practice was to continue what he was doing in his garden until he spotted the bride arriving, and then quickly to enter the vestry, don his surplice – he gardened in his cassock – comb his hair and be ready, all smiles and fertilizer fumes, well before the photographers had finished with the bride at the front of the church.

"in his garden until he spotted the bride arriving"

Everything went well on that fine summer afternoon. The choir met the bride at the door and led her up the aisle to the strains of a marvellous piece of music which the organist made to sound like that from a steam roundabout organ. It was composed by a Frenchman late last century and reflected, I thought, the composer's admiration for Offenbach's can-can.

The first hymn was that puzzling wedding favourite, Blake's "Jerusalem". Most people I've spoken to on the subject are rather hazy as to what Blake was getting at and have no idea at all how the hymn especially applies to a wedding anyway, but it seems to have been drummed into school children for years and years so that in later life, if they are not churchgoers, it's the first thing that enters their heads when the word "hymn" is mentioned. Certainly the large congregation sang the words lustily, including the mothers of the bride and groom, although in their case maybe concentration on singing was more than a little distracted by the fact that they had obviously realized that they were wearing identical hats.

As the service progressed a very friendly choir man next to me kept offering me throat sweets and a continuous series of thumbnail sketches of the wedding party personalities in the congregation. Between the first hymn and the making of the vows I learned, among many other things, that the bride's father was in a shocking mood because he had been overruled and the reception was to be held in the village hall instead of the bar of the Red Lion as he had proposed, and that the bridegroom was so embarrassed and humiliated at the thought of appearing in public in a suit instead of his normal uniform of tattered jeans and tee shirt emblazoned with a risque message that it was only the special appeal of his mother-in-law ("Pull yourself together, you lout") that had enabled him to carry on.

At this point in the service the vicar was asking the assembled company if anyone knew any reason why the marriage shouldn't go ahead. Nobody said anything, of course, but my informant said, well, they wouldn't, would

23

they, not in church, but just wait till people got talking at the reception. That's where you heard the interesting titbits.

The next hymn was quite unknown to me. Apparently the vicar, who had written it, generally managed to sneak it into every marriage service he conducted. It was obviously full of deep meaning and symbolism and had something to do with turning the world into a gigantic community centre. The vicar had not got round to composing a tune for it, so the organist had married it to a well-known tune from Hymns Ancient and Modern – a device that more or less worked if you repeated the last line of each verse.

The choir's final musical contribution was Bach's "Jesu, joy of man's desiring". My temporary colleague said this was a good old potboiler for weddings, although the choir had never really got the hang of it. But it didn't matter much because it was always sung during the period in the service when, the bride and groom and their immediate attendants being temporarily out of sight in the vestry signing the register, the rest of the congregation amused themselves trying to spot members of the family who they'd been avoiding since Grandad's funeral two years ago, and no one would have noticed if the choir were standing on their heads singing "Any old iron".

Perhaps this wedding party were particularly anxious to get away to the reception. The organist played them out with his almost obligatory double version of the Grand March from "Aida" but "Moonlight and roses" wasn't needed this time. In a final chat he warmly invited me to drop in at "the opera house" whenever I was around. I'd be particularly welcome at Sunday Matins, he said, to help the choir keep the vicar in check. The vicar always tried to gabble through the canticles and psalms at twice the speed of everyone else, and often mucked up the whole show.

As I came out of the churchyard a little later, the last car carrying the residue of the wedding party was lurching away along the dirt road from the church and the choir members had long since disappeared by their secret ways. The great calm closed in again as the sleepy sounds of the insects in the tall grass reasserted themselves, and presently I became aware of another sound of contented peace. On a sun-warmed tombstone where I had paused, a large black cat sprawled, purring gently. Had I really just taken part in a big noisy wedding service in this secret place? Already I wondered.

The cat looked up at me, then stretched luxuriously and closed his eyes.

BUSINESS AS USUAL

I NOTICED his name quite by accident while on a summer walking holiday in the West country. It was at the bottom of a notice stuck in the window of a tiny sweet shop in quietest rural Gloucestershire. "Come early" the notice urged in uneven pen and ink capitals, "for great bargains in the Monster Parish Church Jumble Sale. Unrepeatable offers. We open 3 pm sharp". And there was the name of the vicar – Marmaduke. The surname that followed struck no chord with me – I can never remember surnames anyway – but Marmaduke! How many priests, indeed how many men of any kind, are called Marmaduke these days? This simply had to be THE Marmaduke, the one who, twenty years ago, was a curate at my local church. Who could ever forget Marmaduke with his huge bubbling enthusiasms and hopeless muck-ups of everything he ever tried to arrange? His bank holiday parish hikes were a feature that kept our church on the map. Always there was his huge figure with its uncontrollable shock of red hair, striding further and further ahead of us, looking like some rough-hewn wild god, his battered army knapsack swinging askew on his back, its loose straps flapping, and, carried over his shoulder, the rusty black umbrella that he never opened and was never without. We followed him at breakneck speed for miles and miles and hours and hours and when eventually we started losing walkers along the way and Marmaduke had disappeared ahead of the main body of the party with only a few of the hardiest and most determined characters still grimly hanging on to his tail, it usually fell to me to knock at the door of some outlying farmhouse to find out where we were.

Fiasco followed fiasco with Marmaduke. During the winter months he organized grand classical music concerts featuring distinguished singers and instrumentalists – he had a brother who was an orchestral conductor with many obliging musical friends – and on the big night, as often as not, our church choir had to deputize at short notice with a somewhat scaled-down programme of music hall and drinking songs because Marmaduke had given the performers the wrong date or hadn't asked them at all.

People used to come for miles to see our parish pantomime that Marmaduke wrote and produced each year. Lights would explode, scenery collapse and singers fall through trapdoors in the middle of romantic ballads. The good fairy would disappear abruptly on her wire half way through her brave confrontation with the demon king and the sound system would suddenly make Prince Charming sound like a particularly tired and fed-up British Rail station announcer at the end of a long day of cancellations and signal failures. You could always rely on Marmaduke's pantomimes being far more entertaining than any script and there were different hilarious situations at each show. Patrons would come back night after night. No disaster, no unbelievable chaos, ever deterred Marmaduke. He loved his work. He went on arranging even bigger and better muck-ups year after year. He was the most irrepressible, optimistic, cheerful person I'd ever known.

And now I thought I'd caught up with him again. Blundering fate had led me this summer Saturday evening to book for the night at the village's one and only inn. The lady in the sweet shop was most enthusiastic about supplying me with Marmaduke's telephone number and the loan of her telephone – ("A lovely man. The things he does – we never know what's going to happen next") – with the result that I caught him in and confirmed that this was indeed the famous Marmaduke. "How absolutely marvellous" roared the phone, reverberating around the cramped sweet bottles and biscuit tins, "yes! Do come into the choir at Matins tomorrow. We're short – people ill and on holiday and having babies and things. You're a godsend. See you at the church in the morning. Marvellous! By Jove, yes!"

The next morning I reconnoitred the village and soon discovered the church, a venerable shambles surrounded by a huge graveyard full of hefty memorials leaning about at drunken angles under splendid fat oak trees. The main roof of the church was beautifully thatched and the choir vestry had a rusty corrugated iron roof supporting clumps of undernourished weeds, pieces of broken notice board and a tractor tyre.

A teenage choir girl with blatant good looks and a chorister's cap fixed at a most fetching angle on long blonde hair met me at the vestry door and said "Are you the one I'm looking for?" I introduced myself and confirmed that I was the one who had come to help out in the choir. "Marmaduke told me about you. Come with me", she invited, "and I'll fix you up". She took my arm and led me into the choir vestry to a doorless cupboard containing a rail of choir robes. She stood back, eyeing me critically. "Yes", she decided, "my brother's things'll fit you. He's away today. He's a steam buff. He belongs to one of those preserved railways. It's his turn to be fireman". The fireman brother's cassock and surplice fitted me perfectly and it seemed to me they were the smartest and cleanest garments in the cupboard, with none of the faded colours, rents and candle grease splashes displayed by the others. She sensed my appreciation. "My brother's a very natty dresser", she said. "You should see him when it's his turn to be a guard on his railway. He's got a uniform that makes him look like a field marshal". With some pride she started to trail me round the vestry introducing me to other members of the choir, who were now arriving.

She left me with an ancient gentleman who immediately told me he'd been in the choir for seventy years and started regaling me with his recollections of life in the choir from his very first day as a probationer treble. It was rather difficult to see how I was ever going to move on from this gentleman, particularly as he had hemmed me into a corner and kept poking me further in with an authoritative finger as the saga unrolled. Then, just as we'd got to the fateful choir outing on the eve of the second world war, there was a clattering and confusion in the doorway and Marmaduke erupted into the vestry. The wild red hair was still there, the great beaming face still unlined. If anything, he had grown larger than ever. I recalled his handshake and was ready for its crushing intensity. Then the great fist clamped on to my shoulder and propelled me round the vestry to be introduced to the choristers all over again. Finally we arrived back at my choir girl friend who had "fixed me up". Marmaduke's other huge hand drew her to us. "She's our soprano soloist", he said. "Don't know what we'd do without her. She's got a brother in the choir too – real romantic tenor, but he's away today – gone somewhere to drive a steam roller". The soprano soloist had a most attractive smile. "How do you do?" she said.

A tall stooping man with a puzzled contemplative

expression now entered the vestry and, taking not the slightest notice of anyone, climbed out of sight into the organ loft. A sturdy red-faced choir boy who was trying to cram himself into a cassock two sizes too small for him nodded after him and informed me "He's my uncle. He plays the organ and he's wondering".

"Ah", I said.

"He's wondering what the vicar's going to do in the service", he enlarged. "We have to be ready for anything. The vicar gets sort of inspirations all of a sudden".

"During the service?" I asked.

"Yes, right through mostly", confirmed my informant, trying to tuck his cassock together where three buttons had burst off. "Sometimes he changes a hymn just as we're starting to sing and sometimes we get a sermon to start with and another one at the end. Last Sunday he forgot to give out the last hymn, the one we sing to get the collection in. So everyone was clearing off without paying. But the vicar – Orange Marmalade, he's called – he went round the back and got a wheelbarrow and stood outside the door as they came out. He said he wanted a barrow full of money for the organ fund. The organ's got to be looked at – there's some people who sit in the front pew who say it's – er– excruciating or something, and it's not *all* my uncle's fault".

"So no one falls asleep during the service here?" I said.

He winked. "You'll see", he answered gleefully.

Marmaduke having enthusiastically introduced me to the choir for the third time, we all filed in to the well-filled church for morning service which, roughly speaking, was Prayer Book Matins with variations by Marmaduke. In place of the Te Deum we sang two war-like heroic Victorian marching hymns to which Marmaduke beat time with a huge booted foot, and he'd already got half way through the lesson about Elijah getting tough with the prophets of Baal before he realized he'd already read the two lessons set for the service. He carried on unperturbed, however, and said it was a jolly good action story anyway. Finally, just before the blessing, he treated us to a talk on

"Marmaduke beat time with a huge booted foot"

one of his many favourite topics – the return of the tram to English cities. He said tram travel was a splendid way to foster the Christian community spirit – trams didn't pollute like buses or run along the gutter and splash mud over everyone in wet weather. He'd fixed up a slide lecture on the return of the tram in the village hall for Thursday week. A voice from the organ loft bellowed hollowly "Wednesday!" – the organist was also a great tram enthusiast – and Marmaduke beamed and agreed and said, "Of course, yes, Wednesday – er – fortnight – week".

Outside in the churchyard after the service the whole congregation seemed to have gathered. No one was making for home. I found myself in the crowd next to my friend the soprano soloist. "You're coming with us, aren't you?" she asked.

"Where?" I said.

"Marmaduke's walk, of course. Didn't he tell you? It's a regular thing – first Sunday in the month we always have a parish walk. It's great fun. No one knows what'll happen or where we'll end up".

"I know what you mean", I assured her.

Some three hours later I, with some other members of the choir and the organist, had finally given up the chase under a tree by a ditch in the middle of nowhere. "I've never seen a tram", the soprano soloist was saying, handing me half an orange.

"They're marvellous", put in the organist, who was leaning against the tree in a semi-collapsed state. "I remember them. Everything has to get out of the way for them and no hanging about. Trams *get* you there".

I gazed down the seemingly endless sun-baked empty road across the ditch. In my mind's eye I saw the sleek gleaming vehicle on silver rails, effortlessly, swiftly gliding back to the village. I stirred my aching limbs. "I think you're on the right track", I sighed.

FAMILY TRADITIONS

THE NEW young vicar was happily convinced that he was just the man the parish had been waiting for for years. When his fresh, exciting, challenging ideas were instantly and solidly rejected by the congregation and the choir of the village church, he was not in the least discouraged. He realized that they were all busy people who, good souls that they were, gave unstintingly of their precious time to the church but in the past had perhaps not been encouraged and taught how to use that time to best effect in discussion and meditation and experimentation that would result in a live, modern, dynamic rural parish church, relating to today's vital needs and aspirations.

But as my friend George, the church organist, said, if this new man thought he was coming barging into the parish altering all the service times and changing the hymn book and telling people they were an active part of the church and must do parish visiting, and even amalgamating the Monday night men's club with the women's social hour because the church was one great united family, he had another think coming.

And the vicar, all energetic smiles and bubbling with gladsome enthusiasm, had dropped his biggest bombshell in the choir vestry just after Evensong on only the third Sunday of his new ministry. "Splendid singing", he piped, effectually barring the way of the bulk of the choir men who were purposefully moving out of the vestry towards their usual post-Evensong relaxation at the Red Cow, "I've got some really *great* new hymns that I must hear you sing, but, of course, the awful pity is that the congregation are denied so much of the enjoyment you give because there you are hidden away in the choirstalls behind that rather dreadful Victorian screen, when you should be sitting *with* the congregation encouraging them to sing as enthusiastically as you do. I know that you'll all agree with me that we are all one family, one community, not separated, isolated factions. How exciting it will be next Sunday when the choir and congregation are all singing *together* – one united body *in the nave* ..."

Amongst other things, the new vicar's vestry announcement completely upset my arrangement with George. Later that Sunday evening he was supposed to meet me at the station off the last train from London at the start of a two-week holiday I was to spend with him in the village. He wasn't there. No one was there except the porter who urgently trundled me off the platform and locked the gate behind us. Mounting his bike and running over my feet, he suggested that I was likely to find George in the Red Cow with the choir, where he always was if he wasn't in church blasting away on the organ. With a cheery nod he pedalled away into the autumn gloaming and I started on the three-mile trek to the village.

The uproar from the Red Cow assailed me long before I reached that ancient establishment. As I pushed my way into the surging mass in the bar, so many voices were shouting that I couldn't hear a word. A great wave of outrage enveloped me and flowed into the village street. I had met all the choir men before, but no one replied to my "Good evening" and it was only after George himself had related the latest of the new vicar's infamies to me three or four times over that he recognized who I was, and

34

"Likely to find George in the 'Red Cow' with the choir"

then the realization of the off-hand treatment I had been subjected to at the station made him even more outraged with the new vicar. "I don't know ..." he fumed, "I really don't know ... the irresponsible types we get foisted on us as vicars these days – full of stupid ideas and causing people to walk miles and miles ..."

And the new vicar was, unfortunately, as good as his word. When George and I arrived in the choir vestry for the following Sunday morning service – I had a permanent invitation to sing in the choir whenever I stayed in the village – the vicar was hovering around beamingly. He hovered and beamed until all the choir had arrived and robed and then, congratulating our four choir girls on how pretty they looked and affecting not to hear the rather loud rude remarks George was making about people poking their noses into things they knew nothing about, he led us smartly down to the bottom of the church to the last three pews of the middle aisle. "That's the *right* place for the choir to be", he assured us, "backing up the congregation with your splendid volume of sound". He had apparently instructed the sidesmen to keep the three pews clear for us and to move forward any member of the congregation who fancied sitting there. A little trouble had arisen here, however, in the shape of a much revered and feared widow of a local general, who had sat in the same seat at the back of the church for forty years (twenty years with the general and twenty years without) and refused even to consider such nonsense as moving up a row.

The vicar held his smile and instructed us to fall in around her with the result that I found myself sitting next to her in the place where no one had sat since the general had vacated it. I gave her a friendly smile, as I like to give all ladies, formidable or otherwise, but I don't think she quite trusted me because she immediately picked up her handbag from her side and placed it under her seat and gave me a very funny look.

Anyway, the vicar had now bounced back to his stall and announced that this morning everyone was going to have a good sing – a real family effort – and the first hymn would be the one on the piece of green paper that he hoped everyone had been given by the sidesmen. George struck up on the organ, but from the complete lack of any sound from the pews it was obvious that we had come upon one of those hymns that do appear more and more frequently these days via vicars who can't type, use pensioned-off duplicating apparatus and seem to like bits of coloured paper all over the place. If George had got it right on the organ, this hymn went to a tune which appeared to have been knocked together from "Three blind mice" and "Pop goes the weasel". Even by the time we'd reached the seventh verse, the words of which were cramped in an indecipherable mass at the bottom of the bit of green paper, no one seemed to have got into the swing of the thing except the vicar, who ended up breathless and gasped "Wasn't that delightful?" He seemed so elated that for a moment I had the awful feeling that he was going to ask us to sing the whole thing again but, before he could regain his breath, his attention was drawn to a loud deliberate slow tramping sound from the deserted choirstalls behind him. This was made by our sole contralto lady, who always arrived five minutes late for services, always wore riding boots, and had been in the choir for so long and had experienced the idiosyncrasies of so many vicars that, for years now, she had regarded them merely as ships that pass in the night and ignored all their edicts that didn't suit her.

We watched as she determinedly settled herself in her usual seat in the stalls, nodding graciously in response to George's welcoming wave from the organ and spurning the vicar's forceful traffic-police indications that she should proceed to the back of the church to join the rest of the choir.

Doubtless underlining a mental note of what to do with our renegade contralto, the vicar now proceeded with the service and, in the course of the next half hour, we sang with great gusto two well-known hymns from our usual hymn book. I don't think the vicar liked them, though, because he sat down throughout them and appeared to be meditating on his notes for what we used to know as the sermon but which, according to the latest parish magazine, was now to be regarded as a family chat. Just before the family chat we were faced with another "relevant, meaningful" new hymn with a chorus of four words repeated three times on the other side of the bit of green paper. Then the vicar plunged into the chat, walking up and down the aisle and keeping his eye on everyone instead of climbing into the pulpit from where he couldn't be sure whether those people at the back of the church were hanging on his every word or going to sleep behind a pillar or taking a surreptitious glance at the back sports page of their Sunday tabloids.

No one actually joined in the chat; it was one of those where the speaker takes for granted that every one of his listeners agrees with what he is saying. The vicar concluded each of his observations by sweeping us all with his well-held smile and proclaiming "And I'm sure we all agree on *that*" or "And I know you will all fully endorse me on *this*". The agreeing and endorsing went on for some twenty minutes during which time the creaking and clattering from the choir's three back pews became noticeably louder and louder, members finding it a new and uncomfortable experience balancing themselves and their family bible-sized Ancient and Modern hymn books on the slim planks of the pews instead of relaxing in the deep discreet comfort of the choirstalls.

Finally we came to the offertory hymn at the end of the service. It was "Praise my soul the king of heaven" which the vicar said contained some fine words and soon we'd have our own brand-new, more worthy tune to sing them to which was being written specially by a friend of his who, he was sure we would all agree, was really great at hymn tunes. As we rose to sing, my reluctant neighbour, the general's widow, gave a loud sigh of exasperation and started straightening the piece of carpet on the seat where I had been sitting. For the rest of us the hymn, to Sir John Goss's tune, went well as it always had done although we did have a bit of bother in the choir pews. Normally, when the choir were in their official place behind the chancel screen, the collection plate had never been passed round the choirstalls, but a sidesman who thought he was being funny now passed the plate round the three back pews, and there was an awful lot of most unseemly fumbling under cassocks and surplices in an effort to find some money. It completely upset the choir and we missed singing the first two verses of the hymn altogether.

At the next meeting of the parochial church council it turned out that from a vote taken at a large informal parish gathering at the Red Cow it was very clear that, dear friends, soulmates and joyful fellow pilgrims as everyone was, the choir still didn't want to sit with the congregation and the congregation still didn't want to sit with the choir. The vicar tried most earnestly to convince members that they all really agreed with him that his way was right for the coming new century, but the Red Cow decision was immovable and in the end, with a forgiving smile, he agreed to carry on in the present manner "and see how things go".

Things have been back to normal and going well for some months now. The new vicar has rather forgotten the choirstalls issue. He's working on this idea of holding summer open-air services in the Red Cow car park where there will be no divisions of stalls and screens, and the choir will be mixed with the congregation and there will be no way of avoiding the collection or, for that matter, the vicar's family chat.

COACH PARTIES WELCOME

A N UNUSUAL feature of the squat little round-towered Suffolk church was its extremely wide middle aisle. And the vicar was a "middle aisle" man, that is, he never read the lessons from the lectern nor preached from the pulpit. Always he stood in the middle aisle, an ascetic, saintly-looking figure, and presented all he read and said in the sort of matey manner normally experienced in the village pub. He was a "middle aisle" man in everything. He never took sides among the various warring factions in the parish although he was always ready to be enthusiastic about the ideas of one faction provided no one from another faction was within earshot.

The only organization in the parish over which he had no need to be diplomatic was the church choir. Everybody agreed about the choir. The same members had been in the choir for countless years. They always sang the same kind of music in the same way, few could read music and they never learned anything new at all. They were quite dreadful and were held in the highest esteem and regarded with the greatest affection by the whole parish.

They were an institution, a tradition. The vicar knew that he could always rely on the choir being in their places for morning and evening service every Sunday whatever the state of the weather or the world. Indeed, he sometimes thought nostalgically of the pleasant unscheduled Sunday evenings off he had enjoyed in a former parish, when inclement weather or an unmissable

40

television programme had persuaded choir and congregation to give Evensong a miss.

Here, he had no such expectations. Even if the congregation proved fickle, the choir didn't. They were always there in force and expected nothing less than a full choral Evensong and sermon. They'd always been *used* to a full choral Evensong and sermon ...

I had known Mr. Humphreys, the organist and choirmaster, for over twenty-five years (he was always referred to as Mr. Humphreys and no one ever seemed to be sure of his Christian name) and had a standing invitation to sing in the choir whenever I found myself in the vicinity. And one streaming wet and blustery cold Sunday evening in November, fate in the guise of the non-appearance of a local train that had slithered off the rails and ploughed into a field of sugar-beet found me stranded near the village, so I splashed along to Evensong with a few minutes to spare. The pews of the little church were empty and the one bell-ringer of the usual team who had turned up was doing his best tolling the tenor bell in fine funereal style. He grinned at me broadly and invited me to hang my sodden raincoat over the font. At a little distance from him, parked at the back of a deep dim dusty ceremonial chair, was his grandson, a knowing-looking rotund infant wearing a shiny yellow mac and a red-and-white woolly hat shaped like a basin. The rotund one bawled "I jumped in a big puddle!"

"I'll give him puddle", said grandfather.

"I splashed mud all over him", continued the rotund one.

"He really *likes* coming to church", enthused grandfather. "Never misses. It's very encouraging. When we get him into the bell-ringing he'll be a *regular* – not like some of the types we've got in the tower these days. Where are they tonight for instance?"

41

"In the pub!" shouted the rotund one.

"Course, the congregation are no better", mused grandfather. "A drop of rain, and where are they?"

"In the pub!" shrieked the rotund one.

"Anyway, *they're* all here", assured grandfather proudly, nodding towards the choir vestry. "Every one of the choir here as usual. They're doing the Hallelujah chorus tonight. Pity there'll be no one to hear 'em. They should be singing to a big congregation".

"In the pub!" bellowed the rotund one.

There were about a dozen soaking wet choir members in the vestry, all shaking macs and umbrellas at each other and recounting their personal misfortunes experienced while endeavouring to get to Evensong. There was the cosseted car that wouldn't start, the bus that never appeared, the farm lorry that thought it funny to miss you by inches in a narrow lane and drench you with mud, the water-logged "short cut" blocked by a broken down tractor, the automatic umbrella that flew off into the night when you pressed the button and the cat that shot out in front of your bike and caused you to end up in a ditch full of nettles and discarded milk crates.

Nevertheless, everyone had arrived on time and, having squelched around me shaking hands in their usual most friendly welcome, we sorted ourselves into line for what was normally a dignified procession into the chancel – although on this occasion the rubber boots covered in mud with which most members were sensibly equipped would make the dignity a bit difficult.

We were on the point of moving off when the outer vestry door slammed open and a huddled figure, enveloped in a shapeless hooded anorak and carrying a clipboard of rain-pulped papers, staggered in and gurgled "Excuse me,

"staggered in and gurgled 'excuse me, can we look round the church?'"

can we look round the church?" The hood was thrown
back and we saw the face of a very worried young man.
"I've got a coachload of people outside", he revealed.
"We're a church group from London on a tour of some East
Anglian churches. We seem to have lost our way
completely since the last church. We've been dodging

about for miles and miles – what with this weather and Suffolk being so flat, everything looks the same". He sneezed. "This church doesn't seem to be on our itinerary but we thought we could look around now we're here".

The vicar, whose saintly face wore a calm serene expression – probably because he was the only one in the place who hadn't been soaked to the skin getting to church, the vicarage being directly connected to the vestry – explained gently that Evensong was about to begin and the young man said oh dear, yes, of course, he'd forgotten all about Evensong. In their church in London they didn't have Evensong any more. They had a really jolly family service in the morning, and in the evening people dropped in at the church's community centre for games and drama and exciting discussions. The vicar said that his church didn't run to any of those refinements so it was Evensong or nothing. The coach party would be very welcome and his wife could rustle up a cup of tea or something after the service.

The coach party quickly decided that in the circumstances Evensong *was* better than nothing and when the service began we had a congregation that filled half the church, which, as the choir man next to me remarked, wasn't bad for such a dirty night when we'd only expected the bell-ringer and that little fiend of his to be in the congregation.

True, the imported faithful looked a bit bewildered when the Book of Common Prayer was circulated and rather apprehensive when volumes of an early edition of Hymns A & M were provided and the organ began to play, but they were very polite and tried to join in. It was hard to guess what they though of our rendering of Handel's Hallelujah chorus – it was hard to guess what Handel would have thought – but they all sat very still with fixed expressions as if they were afraid of upsetting something and, at the end, someone started to clap. Then, when we reached the sermon and the vicar, despite his saintly unbattered-by-the-elements appearance, started plodding up and down the middle aisle and chatting in his usual pub style, they began to feel really at home.

After the service the coach party was shepherded into the vicarage where the vicar's wife, an expert in providing all sorts of beverages and the most delicious sandwiches and home-made cakes and candies at a moment's notice, was waiting behind an almost indecently laden table. For over an hour the coach party and the choir (the bell-ringer had taken the pub-obsessed infant home) mingled and chatted and finally consumed everything on offer. Then the young man in charge of the party bounded on to one of the vicar's peerless Chippendale dining chairs and said what a splendid finale this was to their tour of East Anglian churches. "Thanks a lot, folks", he concluded, "you certainly must all come up to our church one of these days for our family service. We've got this terrific group that leads the singing – guitars – drums – the lot. You'll really enjoy it". Behind me Mr. Humphreys erupted into a violent coughing fit and smoke from his pipe billowed all over the place ...

The rain had stopped as we went out to their coach to see our guests off and two teenage girls who had been chatting with me assured me that this – what did we call it? – Evensong service thing was quite an idea, especially the bit in the vicarage. They were the best cookies they'd ever tasted. The ones they had at the church community centre would take a lot of getting used to after those Evensong cookies ....

TOM, TOM AND THE BEAUTY

THE CHOIR music library in the country town church where my friend Stanley is organist and choirmaster doesn't conform to any known library standards. It consists of three large cardboard porridge oats cartons crammed with huge, disintegrating wads of music copies all dating from the end of the last century. There are dozens of settings of the canticles and scores of anthems of which Stanley's choir regularly performs two settings and three anthems. Stanley's choir is run on thoroughly democratic lines and, once a quarter, members meet to choose the forthcoming music which always turns out to be the same two settings and three anthems. Everything is very fair and satisfying, however, because although the same music is always chosen, it is chosen each time by different members of the choir so, as Stanley puts it, everyone has a fair crack of the whip, and there's no need to do much rehearsing because everyone has known the stuff backwards for years and years. Everyone has also known everyone else for years and years. The senior members of the choir all went to school together and the junior members are all their children and grandchildren.

Stanley's choir is very traditional and very proud of its past. On the walls in the darker parts of the vestry, between great cupboardsful of fusty pensioned-off cassocks and backless hymn books, are fading photographs of rows of demure-looking Victorian choirboys and extremely proper-looking choir men flanking black-clad vicars and frightened-looking young curates all lined up in the vicarage garden. There are also fading photographs of the same choir men, on their own, looking not half so proper, wearing villainous bowler hats at rakish angles and clutching huge tankards of beer at annual choir outings at Clacton.

Of course, as can be imagined in such a set-up, there are frequent presentations of chiming clocks, electroplated cake stands and crates of alcoholic refreshment to members who have completed incredible numbers of years in the choir and long service records are broken regularly. The latest champion is Top Line Tom, a venerable gentleman, so called because during his sixty-five years' unbroken membership he has never learned to read a note of music and always sings the soprano melody of the hymns in an heroic double-bass voice.

Stanley invited me to Tom's presentation ceremony, as I have often joined the choir during visits and know Tom and the two settings and three anthems very well. The vicar who, unlike so many vicars, is a most enthusiastic supporter of the choir, certainly did us proud. To make sure that the atmosphere was really festive, he invited not only the choir and all known relations and looser connections, but also his usual Rentacrowd, a party of really jolly people who could be depended on to make any function go with a swing and who were never seen in church or, for that matter, anywhere else in the town.

We all gathered in the church hall immediately after Sunday Evensong on a fine cold November evening. As usual there was the long line of trestle tables down the middle of the floor backed by the ladies of the refreshment committee in charge of the most heavenly fare and a collection of bottles with myriad labels, all quite unintelligible to me, all gathered round the splendid resident wooden barrel of beer inscribed in pokerwork "Parish Church – Not to be Taken Away". And as usual there was the hall caretaker on his knees before a large fearsome-looking gas heater which kept on emitting loud popping noises and whistles and no heat whatsoever. The caretaker is very attached to this gas heater and always says that once it gets going the heat will be fantastic, but as far as I know it never has got going and has provided the caretaker with a warm sense of importance and being needed for countless years.

As soon as everyone had squeezed into convenient positions near the food and drink, the vicar, large and beaming and prematurely grasping a large half-eaten sausage roll, clambered on to a chair and made his usual

"Varying the time–honoured practice very slightly by presenting Tom with an automatic toaster"

long-service speech, varying the time-honoured practice very slightly by presenting Tom with an automatic toaster. This was quite permissible, however, because Tom had already collected the usual chiming clock and the cake stand at his fifty- and sixty-year celebrations. So for the next hour everybody ate and drank everything on offer on the trestle tables and nostalgically recalled Tom's early days in the choir when things were exactly the same as they are today.

It was only when the company started to leave the hall, the junior members heading reluctantly for home and the main body eagerly for a second celebration at the Bird in Hand, that I realized I had left a book in the choirstalls. It was a book I'd not ever like to be without called "Tom Brown at Oxford" – Thomas Hughes' not very successful sequel to his "Tom Brown's Schooldays". Today no one seems to have heard of the sequel. It is out of print and gone. But I hold it in very great affection. Magically, it can bring to life one of my favourite historical periods. Merely by dipping into it for a few minutes I am transported back to the Oxford of the eighteen-forties and am at ease amongst all those characters that I have known for years in surroundings that are as real to me as anywhere familiar to me today.

I first came across the novel in my late choirboy days when an earnest and trusting new curate hit upon the idea of slipping "improving" books into the choirstalls in the hope that they would keep the boys reasonably interested and therefore comparatively noiseless during the half-hour sermons which were the fashion in those days. I don't think the ploy worked very well with my colleagues but "Tom Brown at Oxford" certainly worked with me. To this day I have never read the book outside church. Now well worn and frail it still exclusively serves its original purpose of offering me an alternative to enduring a dull sermon or one that I have heard, with minor variations, dozens of times before.

Stanley who, together with every member of the choir, knows all about my attachment to the book, gave me the key of the vestry so that I could recover it immediately and said I'd know where to find him afterwards. I didn't need the key, however. The church was still open and a choir girl was collecting the music copies in the choirstalls and sorting them into familiar-looking frayed bundles. She regarded me with a look of mock reproof that was quite captivating. "You forgot your old friend Tom Brown", she accused. She was in fact our male alto's granddaughter, an utterly charming girl who knew how to look shatteringly attractive even in one of the choir's regulation floursack ladies' gowns. "These copies seem to be disappearing from the bottom up", I remarked, examining a more than usually motheaten pile of anthems. She regarded them affectionately. "Yes", she agreed, "in that lot the bass line has almost completely worn away at the bottom of the pages. I'll have to copy it out and photocopy it and stick it over the rags".

"That makes a lot of work. How good of you", I ventured admiringly.

"Oh, it's nothing". She smiled her delightful smile. "I did the same thing with some other copies last month, only they were disappearing from the top and it was the soprano line that you couldn't read".

"Marvellous", I beamed, enchanted.

"It doesn't really matter, of course", she explained, placing the wads in criss-cross fashion and carrying them to the music library in the porridge oats cartons. "After all, we only *hold* the copies while we're singing. No one actually follows the music – Stanley says if we don't know it by now we never will – but it does look nicer from the point of view of the congregation if we're holding tidy copies and not things that look like bits of rag". She stepped back into the choirstalls and scooped up a collection of non-ecclesiastical literature that the choir members had left lying around on their seats – a Dalton's Weekly, a Heavy Horse World, two elderly issues of Woman's Own, a mail order catalogue, a Barbara Cartland paperback and a list of local football fixtures. She placed them in two tidy piles at the end of each back stall. "They need something to read during the sermon", she observed.

I recalled the earnest young curate of my boyhood days who had inaugurated a similar scheme. Perhaps someone like him had once been at this church also. "Have the choir always read during the sermon?" I asked, intrigued. "Good gracious, yes", she confirmed. "Well, ever since the chancel screen was put up and the bottom of the choir was hidden from the congregation". She laughed softly, with guileless hazel eyes. "And the screen was put up to commemorate Queen Victoria's diamond jubilee".

"You seem to know a lot about the choir history", I said.

"You know", she explained, "my grandfather has been in the choir for ages and ages – he got his chiming clock over five years ago – and he can tell all sorts of stories. I was brought up on them. Mind you -" she added, frowning, "regarding reading during the sermon, some of the choir get a bit annoyed these days when the vicar's away and we have this retired priest to take the services. You see, it's all to do with cart horses. The vicar's always been very keen on cart horses. He's even talked about getting rid of his old car and turning his garage into a stable so that he can keep a Shire horse as a pet". The delightful smile returned. "They are so lovely, don't you think? – great big gorgeous glossy things with huge fluffy hooves – but the buses are so awful round here and they've closed the railway, so he feels he must keep his car".

"I'm with you", I said.

"Oh!" She suddenly glanced up at the vestry clock which permanently indicates five to six, and down at her watch. "You'll be missing the doings at the Bird in Hand".

"I don't really drink", I said

51

She took off her choir robe and hung it up. It turned back into a floursack like all the others. "Anyway", she resumed, "the vicar goes to all the horse shows he can find and lately he's been doing a bit of commentating in the heavy horse classes at some of the smaller shows, but they're often held on Sundays and sometimes he takes a day off".

"And you're left with this retired man", I concluded.

"Yes, and that's where the trouble comes in". Her eyes sparkled and her smile was magic. "He doesn't seem to know how to preach. No sooner is he up in the pulpit than he's down again. There's simply no time to read anything".

"It's the way things are going", I sympathized. "Priests seem to have lost the art of preaching. Nowadays it's all meaningful dialogues over cups of coffee at the back of the church after the service".

As we prepared to leave she locked up the organ console after removing a half-bar of chocolate, some liquorice allsorts and a tomato from the lower keyboard. "Stanley always has this trouble with eating", she explained. "No matter what he's eaten before the service, by the time we get to the anthem he's ravenous so he keeps a little store in his music cupboard. It doesn't matter what it is as long as he can eat it".

Suddenly she went back into the choirstalls. "You're forgetting him again", she called out, "poor old Tom Brown". She re-appeared, holding my battered old friend. I went to take it eagerly. She opened it and turned the pages. "When I came back here to clean up tonight I started to read it", she said. "It looks rather interesting. You've carried it around for years. I'd like to discover its secret. Would you let me borrow it?"

I looked at Tom Brown. I looked at our male alto's beautiful granddaughter. "Why, of course", I capitulated. "With pleasure. Yes! Delighted!"

JEREMIAH TOMKINS

NOBODY REALLY knows why my cousin Harry's cat is called Jeremiah Tomkins. There have always been cats in Harry's family and they've all been called Jeremiah Tomkins. There is a story that somewhere around the middle of last century there was a wayward daughter who gave up attending the local Church of England with her family and joined the Methodist church, to which she was drawn by an attractive young minister named Jeremiah Tomkins, and that the first cat called Jeremiah Tomkins was named after him. Harry, however, says this is only a scurrilous rumour put about by an outraged grandfather who couldn't bear the thought of a member of his family going to perdition with the Methodists and who simply hated cats.

The truth may never be known, but there is no doubt that the present-day Jeremiah Tomkins is a worthy successor to such a long line of forebears – a shaggy rusty black, a mighty hunter and fighter, an unbeaten defender of a wide territory around Harry's house, a battered, cheerful, clever feline much admired by Harry and his wife and properly respected by the family Alsatian.

And on this particular evening Jeremiah Tomkins and his kind were very much in my mind. I was taking part in a committee meeting to plan the first-ever animal thanksgiving service to be held in the village church where Harry is organist and choirmaster. The committee was composed almost entirely of choir members. All the committees in Harry's parish are composed almost entirely of choir members because the choir is the only efficient organization in the parish and generally runs the whole place. I had been invited to join this committee because I'd been involved elsewhere in animal services, and anyway I always sang in the choir on my not infrequent visits to Harry.

The single non-choir member apart from the vicar, who acted as chairman, was The Committee Lady – an elderly wispy character who is always darting about the church with the speed and uncertainty of direction of a dragonfly, with her arms full of flower vases, parish magazines, forgotten umbrellas and scarves and wildly wriggling infants who think the family communion service is a fun fair. Like the choir members, she serves on every committee in the parish. Her speciality is to arrive half an hour late for a meeting, request an immediate recapitulation of what she has missed, and then hold the floor for another half hour to explain why the rest of the committee should think exactly as she does.

The vicar, as chairman, said very little. A tall, vague, puzzled-looking bachelor of uncertain age, with a row of vintage car club badges pinned across his cassock, he is one of those clerics who dismiss the animal kingdom as a baffling eccentricity of the Creator, and any regard or concern for that kingdom by humans as an even more baffling eccentricity. In fact his only previous connection with animals in the parish had been the erection of a NO DOGS warning in the churchyard. But he is an incurable innovator of boundless optimism and, having tried to fill the church with motorbike services – "Your motorbike is welcome" – and poetry readings and religious panel games in place of choral Evensong with scant success, he was quite willing to see what the animals could do. He smiled encouragingly at the committee and kept on eating salted peanuts from a little earthenware bowl marked CAT.

We were well into the second hour of the meeting and The Committee Lady, having delivered herself of her usual half-hour directive which included a demand that on the day of the service all the kneelers should be removed from the pews and the mats from the church porch in case of "doggie accidents", had taken out her knitting and left us to manage as best we could. Various suggestions had been put forward, puzzled over and gently dropped, and then our bass soloist solemnly knocked out his pipe on the sculpted head of an eighteenth-century vicar that glared at him in a most disapproving manner, and asked "What about the music? What do you sing for animals? I once had a ferret who used to go berserk when I whistled 'O perfect love'. We'll have to be careful about the music".

I suggested that about the only hymn that our hymn book seemed to offer in that line was "All things bright and beautiful". The vicar turned up the hymn and looked at it as if he'd never seen it before – and this may have been a fact, for this vicar, a rigid devotee of modern hymnology, never sang a Victorian hymn and during the singing of such (Harry chose the hymns) would stand absently watching the chancel ceiling and twirling the tassel of his cassock girdle faster and faster.

Harry, after some thought, stepped into the breach and said that "bright and beautiful" really only half applied to Jeremiah Tomkins. He was bright all right – he could probably talk if he cared to – but as far as beautiful was concerned, he'd never be that with his motheaten coat and shredded ears ...

A member of the choir who worked at the local brewery said it was the exact opposite with the brewery's new one-

and-a-quarter ton Shire horse, Bomber. Bomber certainly had a sort of massive beauty, no doubt about that, but he was so stupid that he could lose his way walking across the stable yard.

The vicar, who doubtless felt that by this time some contribution was due from him, now proposed that we should settle for "All things bright and beautiful" as the opening hymn of the service – and had anyone got any suggestions for further, preferably more modern, meaningful hymns? A contralto lady who was very poetically minded and had once had some verses about walking along a canal bank in the pouring rain published in the local paper (she'd had dozens of copies made, many of which were still stuck all over the vestry) coyly suggested that she should write one or two animal hymns about which she already had some simply heavenly ideas.

After a short meditation on this the committee grunted its usual relieved approval when faced with awkward situations for which they could think of no other solution, and our bass soloist suggested that the final hymn should be "Fight the good fight" because this was the favourite hymn of his granny who kept three dogs, two cats, a snake and a canary and loved all animals ...

A week or two later, when I arrived at the church for the animal thanksgiving service, the bass soloist's boxer dog gave me his usual enthusiastic welcome, pitching me headlong into the vestry where the choir and their pets were joyously assembling. Dogs of all shapes and sizes (mostly very large) were straining at leashes trying to establish contact with a number of cats who regarded them loftily from baskets and cardboard boxes with holes in them. Someone had put a frog in a plastic box on the piano, and a rabbit and a budgerigar studied each other

"Jeremiah, recognizing a fake, promptly nipped him"

quizzically from their respective containers on the vicar's desk. The vicar plodded about looking utterly bewildered and, coming up to Jeremiah Tomkins, assumed the tone he always used (quite unsuccessfully) when trying to charm bawling babies in the church creche. "Hello, pretty Tiddles", he crooned, poking his finger into Jeremiah Tomkins' basket, and Jeremiah, recognizing a fake, promptly nipped him. In fact Jeremiah Tomkins had had the vicar summed up within hours of his arrival in the parish. Jeremiah was an old hand at coming to church.

57

Living next door to the church, he had staked his claim to the territory long before the advent of the present incumbent, and each Sunday at Matins took up his position on Harry's organ stool from where he regarded the vicar with an unblinking stare throughout the service.

At first the vicar found this rather disconcerting, but after a time learned to resist the futile temptation of trying to outstare Jeremiah Tomkins.

And so the first-ever animal thanksgiving service at Harry's church took place and was a great success. The vicar sat amidst the huge congregation of man and beast and wondered, amazed, why so many people came to a service like this when only half-a-dozen or so turned up for his motorbike services and poetry readings and religious panel games. He didn't understand it at all but he did understand that the church was full. He felt almost elated as he stood at the church door after the service. Not only did he have an appreciative word for every human, he acknowledged the animals, at least the dogs and cats. In his creche voice he addressed each dog as " – er, Dog" and each cat as "Tiddles".

A few days after the service Harry and I went to lunch at the vicarage. As the vicar greeted us, a small knowing-looking tabby cat skittered around his feet chasing a ball of paper. The vicar noticed our looks of amazement. "It was left over from the animal service", he explained. "It appears to have come on its own. It seems to have adopted me". He smiled in a puzzled manner. "The vicarage cat", he pondered. "I wonder if he'll come to church like – er – your cat, Harry?"

"What's its name?" I asked, intrigued. The vicar seemed slightly surprised by my question. "Tiddles, I suppose", he said.

THE SUPERB CHOIR

WHEN A choir, choirmaster and organist work together as a team, all generally goes well with them and the only threat of disharmony comes from the vicar. Vicars normally fall into two categories – those who insist on being the power behind the throne and dictate the musical policy of the church down to the final amen, and those who are only too pleased to let the choir get on with it as long as they don't do anything too outrageous and upset the more prickly members of the congregation. These latter vicars are well liked by choirs and can depend on solid backing from members for just anything they want to do in the parish as long as it has nothing to do with the music. The former types are resented by the choir and are apt to receive vitriolic notes and phone calls from members to which they reply in equally unpleasant and unbending tones until either the organist and choirmaster or the vicar resigns, or the whole choir walk out and invade a neighbouring church choir who don't want them.

Such a calamity recently overtook the very happy choir of which my friend Wally is organist and choirmaster. The vicar at Wally's church has been there for years and years and is definitely of the "leave 'em alone" brigade as far as the choir is concerned. His only connection with the music is his part in singing the versicles which he's never been able to accomplish without going flat, but he doesn't *know* he goes flat – he's such a pleasant man that nobody ever tells him. Consequently life has flowed smoothly for Wally's choir and they enjoy the affection of the congregation for the comfortably familiar. It must be said of course, and Wally himself would agree, that his is not a choir of exalted standards. They mainly lead the congregation in the singing of favourite hymns and perform a jolly rumbustious Victorian anthem at two at Christmas, Easter and harvest. They've never entered a choral competition or performed at a concert, and the only singing they ever do outside the church is when they go round the pubs at Christmas singing carols in aid of a local old people's home and a sanctuary for retired horses.

On the other hand the choir of the neighbouring Parish Church are superb. Indeed they are always referred to in the local paper and by members themselves as superb. The opening services of local arts festivals and prestigious civic occasions are by general consent held at this church so that the event may be graced by the performance of the superb choir, and no one with any artistic pretensions at all would go anywhere else to get married.

The superb choir are always busy giving impeccable recitals and winning choral competitions all over the place and, in fact, are so busy that quite often they have not been able to find time to sing at the actual church services, but the congregation have always realized that the inconvenience is a small price to pay for such a superb choir.

It was the advent of a new vicar at the Parish Church that upset everything recently. He seemed to think that, superb or not, church choirs were meant mainly to sing at church services and not to be too annoyed if the congregation's singing was not up to standard and flawed the superb sound of the choir. The new vicar decreed that forthwith the choir should sing at every choral service despite the pressing calls of recitals, competitions and festivals.

He outraged the whole choir. They simply could not conceive how anyone could be such a philistine as to try to impede such a superb choir from spreading abroad their superb art. The choirmaster promptly withdrew his choir from the church and, looking around with a professional eye, lighted on Wally's church as the one with the best acoustics for miles. There and then he decided that this church should instantly benefit from the singing of his superb choir.

Thus it was that one Sunday evening immediately after Evensong the vestry of Wally's church was invaded by the whole superb choir. Their choirmaster had a word with the vicar, who promptly passed him on to Wally and hurried away down the church to shake hands with the congregation. Even before he had properly cornered Wally behind the vestry piano, the choirmaster was imparting the good news of the advent of his choir. It would, he explained, enable Wally and his singers to achieve things undreamed of far, far beyond mere hymn singing. A whole new world would be opened up. They would be thrilled. He had got deep into details of when and how future choir rehearsals would take place under the new regime before Wally succeeded in halting him in mid-sentence to say no thank you very much, but if any members of the superb choir would like to join his choir and learn how to sing hymns properly, they would be welcome – and indeed especially welcome to come and swell the crowd and have a go at the carol singing round the pubs at Christmas.

Stunned, the choirmaster regarded Wally, aghast. What was the Church of England coming to? Everywhere there were philistines – philistines wherever you looked. Was there *no* appreciation of the higher things any more – no respect – no ambition? He moved away amidst his shocked singers.

"Choir practice seven thirty Fridays", called Wally after them. "We always have a good sing".

Having seen off the last of the congregation, the vicar returned hesitantly to the vestry and seemed surprised that no member of the superb choir was in evidence. "All – er – fixed up then?" He switched a general smile in Wally's direction. "I – er – gather that they plan to join our choir. Some little bother at the Parish Church, I believe".

"a worried vicar of the Parish Church telephoned him with an urgent appeal"

Wally put him right on the situation, concluding "So we won't be seeing *them* again", and the vicar visibly brightened as the company left the church for their evening television viewing or rather more colourful argument at the Dog and Duck. The vicar, however, had not heard the last of the affair. The next evening a worried vicar of the Parish Church telephoned him with an urgent appeal. No doubt he had heard of the annoying business of the choir's walking out. In a way he was rather glad they'd gone – he wouldn't have to sit through any more twenty-minute anthems or be expected to enjoy singing favourite hymns to tunes he'd never heard of – but the immediate difficulty was that there was an important choral wedding booked at the Parish Church for Saturday and he simply couldn't present the party with no organ and empty choirstalls. Could his colleague's choir and organist help out?

As was his wont in circumstances like these, Wally's vicar passed the Parish Church vicar straight on to Wally. "You'll catch him in if you phone him immediately", he urged, and put the phone down quickly. He'd done his bit. Whatever the outcome, he would smile and say he was sure it was for the best. He settled down happily to his book on steam traction in the nineteenth century.

Meanwhile the vicar of the Parish Church, who had never heard Wally's choir sing and knew nothing whatsoever about them, was telling Wally over the phone how privileged he would feel to have such a choir singing at the wedding on Saturday, and Wally, who was thinking that, after all, it would make a change from singing round the pubs, was waiting for a break in the flow of flattery to say yes. He enjoyed wedding services. He was always intrigued by the unbelievable hats chosen by the mothers of the bride and groom and by the behaviour of guests who were not used to being in church, who either tiptoed everywhere and tended to bow to everyone in a cassock, or bawled across the church to each other as if they were at a football match.

Wally's choir backed him magnificently on Saturday. Every member was present at the Parish Church, where the vicar treated them with a deference and overwhelming friendliness that even surprised him. Indeed, he hadn't finished his speech of welcome before he suddenly realized that it was almost time for the wedding party to arrive and, apologizing profusely, trotted off to do some more welcoming in the church porch.

Some members of the choir were leafing through the music to be sung. A large bass with a scrubbed, shiny red face and cigarette butt wedged behind his ear rumbled "What's this Latin thing? We don't do this kind of stuff at weddings. We don't do it at all – not Latin stuff".

Wally reassured him and the rest of the choir. "Don't worry about that. It's all in unison, anyway. I'll play it on the organ and you follow where you can. You'll soon pick it up".

"And then, this hymn", persisted the bass. "We know the words but I bet no one's heard the tune". Wally gave it a brief glance as he adjusted his large spotted bow tie before the equally spotted vestry mirror. "That's all right", he said, and, raising his voice above the usual winter-sale din that always rose from his choir as the time of a service approached, "we'll do our tune to the first hymn. And the final amen looks a funny kind of thing. Forget it. We'll do Stainer's sevenfold. Can't beat the old sevenfold. And I'll play 'em out with the French thing you all like", he concluded comfortably.

"That thing that sounds like the Wurlitzer down at the Odeon when I was a lad", clarified the big bass. "Just the job. They'll like that".

Whether anybody in the wedding party ever realized that the original choice of music had been re-vamped is doubtful. The wedding was one of those high fashion affairs, the sun shone brightly, and afterwards, during the photography session in the churchyard, everyone kept falling over half-submerged gravestones and exclaiming "Lovely!" and "Gorgeous!" and "Jolly good show!"

Wally was sure that they were talking about the choir, a belief heightened by the vicar who, providing against the possibility of the superb choir never returning to the fold, assured Wally that he'd *never* enjoyed singing with a choir so much – particularly the first hymn to that grand old tune he hadn't heard since the days he'd been a choirboy. Later he was surprised to realize that he'd really meant every word he'd said.

And having failed to gatecrash any other churches, the superb choir did return to the Parish Church and, despite all their other engagements, they do now manage to sing at all the Sunday services. Just occasionally, however, a very important concert engagement does clash with a wedding and then the Parish Church vicar happily, indeed eagerly, phones Wally and Wally and his choir roll up and put on another jolly good show of the vicar's kind of music.

THE CARVED WORK THEREOF

IT IS always a pleasant experience to visit my Uncle Bert's village church. It's not Uncle Bert's church really, of course, but it's named after such an obscure saint that I can never remember his name or what he did, whereas I know Uncle Bert and what he does very well. He's always getting his name into the papers at the foot of explosive letters of objection on every subject you can think of, and some you would never have thought of. He writes regularly to bishops and cabinet ministers and, as a representative of the choir on the parochial church council, enlivens the meetings of that otherwise somnolent body no end with fiery challenges and unanswerable questions. When the vicar wants something to be done in the church and not just argued about at the P.C.C, he sends for Uncle Bert and everything works out wonderfully. But recently the vicar sent for Uncle Bert once too often.

The choirstalls at Uncle Bert's church were what the vicar described as "nearing the end of their useful life". If he was referring to their ability to accommodate members of the choir and their music, he was wrong. They had solidly done their job for over a hundred and fifty years and were sturdily capable of continuing to do so, but if the vicar was referring to their capacity to accept any more choirboys' names carved into them, he was right. There was now hardly a square inch of uncarved surface remaining. Anyway, the vicar, a young man who tended to regard church choirs as "groups" and preferred seeing them perched on chrome and plastic stools backed by a guitar and drums rather than in choirstalls accompanied by the organ, felt he now had a good case for getting rid of the stalls and taking a step towards the chrome and plastic stools.

The fatal mistake he made was to ask Uncle Bert to arrange things so that the parishioners would be in favour of the removal of the stalls and everything would proceed smoothly. Normally Uncle Bert could be relied on to employ his undoubted expertise in favour of the vicar, but this time the vicar's suggestion horrified him. Weren't there the names of five generations of his family carved on those stalls? Indeed, hadn't every member of the present choir at least one ancestor whose name appeared among the scores immortalized on the stalls? Good heavens! This was history. At places like Eton College, they were proud of all those names carved all over the place. The parish was proud of its church choir. It revered the mementoes of its past choir members. Uncle Bert would certainly have nothing to do with the removal of the stalls. Indeed, Uncle Bert would, as usual, be positive. He would oppose their removal – organize the opposition.

During the following weeks, he wrote long impassioned letters to the local paper and the county magazine, extolling the "priceless relics" that the village church contained in the shape of its "unique choirstalls where generations of local families have sung and left their names engraved for all time".

A young press reporter, who had himself sung in the choir as a boy soprano but had never realized that week after week he was lolling about in a priceless relic, was despatched to the vicar to get his views. The vicar took him into the church, confronted him with the stalls, and asked him to "just take an honest look at the awfulness of it all". The young reporter looked and found his own name – scratched on the back of his seat, he remembered, with an instrument attached to his pocket knife designed for taking stones out of horses' hooves.

"Carving! I ask you!" appealed the vicar tensely. "Just scratched, scrawled, illiterate graffiti. You will, I'm sure, appreciate my anxiety to have these unworthy things removed". The young reporter nodded noncommittally and allowed himself to be conducted around the church to be shown some of its finer features he had never noticed as a boy – the mediaeval stained glass, the eighteenth-century font, the rare brass they had discovered when removing a piece of motheaten Victorian stair carpet from the vicar's stall, the memorial to a famous landscape painter whose marble likeness now peered gloomily from behind the packing-case-like erection housing the organ blowing apparatus. The vicar concluded the tour by demonstrating the new apricot-coloured concealed lighting of which he was very proud, having installed it himself. How, he asked, could those awful choirstalls be allowed any longer to exist amongst all this beauty and artistry ...? As the young reporter departed, the vicar felt sure he had created the right impression and that he could depend on a most sympathetic supportive article in the local paper.

I learned the story so far from Uncle Bert when I arrived for a week's holiday with him, just as the choirstalls squall was developing into a fully-fledged storm.

News of the controversy had seeped into some sections of the national press, and Uncle Bert reckoned that lately there'd hardly been a moment during the day when some stranger wasn't standing staring at the choirstalls. Even regular members of the congregation came into the church at odd times during the week to look at the choirstalls that they'd seen every Sunday for years and years. Visitors from far and near took photographs from all angles and not a few sprawled on the chancel floor eating sandwiches and making drawings and copious notes. The choir, who liked their choirstalls and wanted to retain them much more than they did their vicar, had seized on the opportunity for publicity and arranged for two of their most attractive sopranos to be seen lovingly polishing the stalls at frequent intervals during the weekends when visitors were most numerous. Uncle Bert said that to his knowledge the stalls hadn't been polished for at least twenty years, so the girls found plenty of genuine work to do and the whole performance was most convincing right down to the hoovering of the odd bits of carpet that the choir members had introduced over the years to make the seating more comfortable. Total strangers came and saw and smiled encouragingly at the girls and went away seething with anger at the insensitiveness of the vicar.

Soon after my arrival on Sunday afternoon, Uncle Bert said we should go along to the church to see what was happening, and we found what was now the usual crowd of sightseers milling around the choirstalls with the vicar vainly attempting to draw them off to view the other church features. No one seemed the slightest interested in stained glass or fonts or even the apricot concealed lighting. They'd come to see the choirstalls, and that was that.

A small group of visitors huddled on their haunches as a large, round, bass choir gentleman on his knees pointed out a list of four names scratched deeply at the foot of one stall. "My grandfather and three great-uncles", he announced proudly, "all boys in the choir a hundred years ago. See what they've written" – and he pointed even lower to a single word "Champions" – "How about that?" he beamed proudly.

"Champion whats?" asked a little man, squinting through a reading glass two inches from the wording.

"My grandfather and great-uncles were champions at everything", answered the bass, in a tone of finality. "And look at this". He pointed further along the panel to a name

"A small group of visitors huddled on their haunches."

that began with "Charlie" but faded out into some indecipherable hieroglyphics and ended up as a large hole bored right through the wood. "A marvellous bloke, was Charlie", recollected the bass. "In the choir for forty-six years. Couldn't sing a note. Completely tone-deaf but he organized the finest choir outings we've ever had, and when he was captain of the choir football team we only lost two matches in five seasons. There aren't many choir men around like Charlie these days".

At this point the choir's oldest member, a man who had been the most popular lead in the local dramatic society before the second world war, made an impressive entrance and started telling the crowd heart-warming tales of choir members commemorated on the stalls, many of whom he had known and still sadly missed – "fine, wonderful colleagues and friends, the like of whom I don't expect to meet again". Everyone gathered round and shook his hand amidst a frenzy of flashlight photography, during which the vicar quietly slipped away with a deeply thoughtful expression on his face.

Uncle Bert reckoned that things were going well. "Let's go home and have some tea", he said, "and then come back and sing in the choir at Evensong. It's going to be good tonight".

Two hours later we were back in church, crammed into the choirstalls, which reeked of polish and by this time were very slippery. The vicar gave the choirstalls (or it may have been the choir) an unfathomable look and announced the opening hymn to a congregation rather larger than the usual dozen and a half sterling characters who regularly managed to resist the lure of television for an hour on Sunday evenings. The pews were overflowing and a crowd of people, including a small badly-behaved infant and a large well-behaved dog, were marshalled at the back of the church.

Never having had to cater for such a large congregation, the supply of hymn books had given out and people were looking three over a book, although after singing the first verse of a rather unfamiliar hymn most gave up trying to read the second verse and started gazing vaguely all over the place or taking a more particular interest in a man with a press camera, who kept on crawling up and down the side aisle and appearing round the pillars. I had a distinct impression that Uncle Bert's efforts on behalf of the choirstalls were reaching a climax.

As usual, the singing of the psalm and canticles was left to the choir and, while we were singing the Nunc Dimittis, the small badly-behaved infant scrabbled up to the choir screen and glared at us, waving a plastic gun in a most menacing way until the large well-behaved dog appeared and nudged him back to his place.

And so we reached the sermon. The vicar, in his most chatty manner, said how good it was to be able to welcome so many visitors to this historic church. Being rather in the backwoods it had, perhaps, been overlooked in the past but now he was absolutely delighted to report that just before the start of this evening's service he had been invited by the editor of a most prestigious national magazine to contribute a major article on the church and its treasures and traditions – treasures and traditions that must be preserved and guarded, for while ever looking ahead the church must not forget its past from which it was moulded ... the vicar chatted on and on. He finished strongly. "But whatever a church possesses, let us always remember that it is its members – people – that really matter – the faithful throughout the ages. On seeing our historic, indeed unique, choirstalls – an ever-present witness – we are vividly reminded ... Let us not forget their service ..." Uncle Bert grinned hugely at me. He leaned forward between the two attractive choir girls. "No need to do any more polishing, girls", he whispered. "All that polish will last for years".